At the foot of Bramble Cottage garden

The Northumberl... ...ies dwell

Far past the garden gate

Down by the wishing well

Skating on a puddle
The Laughing Fairy plays

She loves the winter weather
And the icy puddle days

She giggles and shrieks

Spins, slides and twirls

A show she puts on

For the fairy boys and girls

She never cries and never lies
She always laughs and smiles
The Laughing Fairy is famous now
In fairy lands for miles

She laughs when she is flying

She giggles when she is swimming

She laughs when she is losing

And giggles when she is winning